In honor of my husband, Dr. Robert C. Brooks, and his journey with cancer. His strength and devotion to our family gave us all courage to bravely face the present and the opportunities that await us in the future. My love for him is unconditional, undying, and unending.

Much love and thanks to our daughter, Carly, and granddaughters, Emmerson and Sicily, who are the real creators of this book. It was their ideas and enthusiasm for filling a canvas bag with memorable surprises that served as my inspiration. This act of love gave us happiness in the midst of challenge and also gave us purpose, living for today and having optimism for tomorrow. This is a blessing we hold on to.

- Mary Brooks

www.mascotbooks.com

Bampa's Bag

For more information, please contact:
Mascot Books
560 Herndon Parkway #120
Herndon, VA 20170
info@mascotbooks.com

Library of Congress Control Number: 2014949232

CPSIA Code: PRT1014A
ISBN-13: 978-1-62086-840-9

Printed in the United States

BAMPA'S BAG

Mary Brooks *Mary Brooks*

illustrated by
Caitlyn Knepka

When we found out our grandpa had cancer, we didn't know what that meant.

Mommy told us that "Bampa" would be seeing doctors to help him get healthy again.

Bampa would go to treatments and get medicine to help him feel better.

We wondered what we could do to help him.

Mommy thought we should put together a bag of fun things for Bampa to take with him to the cancer center each week.

She bought a canvas bag for us to decorate. We had fun putting our hands in the paint. We called it "Bampa's Bag."

Then we decided what things to put into the bag.

Each week we spent time choosing several special surprises for Bampa.

One thing that was always in Bampa's Bag was a word search we created just for him.

It helped to keep Bampa's mind off of his cancer.

It was fun to come up with the words that Bampa had to find and circle each week.

We usually put drawings and craft projects in Bampa's Bag.

Sometimes we put treats, photos of us, or something we'd done that would make Bampa proud.

Our grandma, "Gimmie," said that some things made Bampa laugh until he cried.

She also told us sometimes Bampa just cried.

Mommy told us we were too young to be doctors and heal Bampa with medicine.

But she said we were just right to heal him with love.

Bampa is our hero.

His doctors are doing everything they can to treat his cancer.

Gimmie is doing everything she can to keep Bampa healthy.

Bampa is doing his best to take good care of himself.

And Mommy will continue helping us with the Bampa Bag so we can keep giving Bampa all the love and joy we can.

The Bampa Bag makes Bampa happy,
and it makes us happy to know we
are helping him.

Bampa's Bag may not cure our Bampa of cancer, but it is our way of helping, offering hope, and encouraging healing.

We now understand that our Bampa is living with cancer, and we are living the journey with him because we love him.

ABOUT THE AUTHOR

Mary is a retired West Des Moines, Iowa, educator. She taught junior high language arts classes for 34 years. She obtained three degrees from Drake University. Mary's current role as Head Judge of the Scripps National Spelling Bee–and her service in various capacities since 1972–earned her a spot in the Iowa Hall of Pride, the first and only one of its kind in the nation. Mary loves to read, and she has always wanted to be a writer. The story of Bampa's Bag made it possible for her to pursue this dream. Other passions of Mary's include being the best "Gimmie" ever, walking, golfing, serving and supporting several philanthropies, and believing in "lucky" pennies.